THE BOUGH ON THE TREE

THE TREE IN THE WOOD

Book 4

By the same editors

THE TREE IN THE WOOD
A Junior Anthology

Book 1   The Egg in the Nest

Book 2   The Nest on the Twig

Book 3   The Twig on the Bough

Book 4   The Bough on the Tree

THE BOUGH
ON THE TREE

Poems chosen by

RAYMOND O'MALLEY

& DENYS THOMPSON

Decorations by Julia Ball

THE TREE IN THE WOOD: BOOK 4

FRANKLIN WATTS, INC.
575 Lexington Avenue
New York, N.Y. 10022

watts
INTERNATIONAL

Copyright © Chatto and Windus Ltd 1966
Library of Congress Catalog Card Number: 68-19244

Published 1966 by
Chatto and Windus Ltd, London
First American Publication 1968
by Franklin Watts, Inc.
1 2 3 4

Printed in the United States of America

CONTENTS

§ 1

§ 2

§ 3

§ 4

The egg was in the nest,
The nest was on the twig,
The twig was on the bough,
The bough was on the tree,
The tree was in the wood:
And the green grass grew all round,
around, around,
And the green grass grew all round.

Armies in the Fire

The lamps now glitter down the street;
Faintly sound the falling feet;
And the blue evening slowly falls
About the garden trees and walls.

Now in the falling of the gloom
The red fire paints the empty room:
And warmly on the roof it looks,
And flickers on the backs of books.

Armies march by tower and spire
Of cities blazing, in the fire;
Till as I gaze with staring eyes,
The armies fade, the lustre dies.

Then once again the glow returns;
Again the phantom city burns;
And down the red-hot valley, lo!
The phantom armies marching go!

Blinking embers, tell me true,
Where are those armies marching to,
And what the burning city is
That crumbles in your furnaces!

R. L. STEVENSON

The Strange Wild Song

He thought he saw a Buffalo,
 Upon the chimney-piece:
He looked again, and found it was
 His Sister's Husband's Niece.
'Unless you leave this house,' he said,
 'I'll send for the Police!'

He thought he saw a Rattlesnake,
 That questioned him in Greek;
He looked again, and found it was
 The Middle of Next Week.
' 'The one thing I regret,' he said,
 'Is that it cannot speak!'

He thought he saw a Banker's Clerk
 Descending from a bus;
He looked again, and found it was
 A Hippopotamus.
'If this should stay to dine,' he said,
 'There won't be much for us!'

He thought he saw a Kangaroo
 That worked a coffee mill;
He looked again, and found it was
 A Vegetable Pill.
'Were I to swallow this,' he said,
 'I should be very ill!'

He thought he saw a Coach-and-four
  That stood beside his bed;
He looked again, and found it was
  A bear without a Head;
'Poor thing,' he said, 'poor silly thing!
  It's waiting to be fed!'

He thought he saw an Albatross
  That fluttered round the Lamp;
He looked again, and found it was
  A Penny-Postage-Stamp.
'You'd best be getting home,' he said,
  'The nights are very damp!'

LEWIS CARROLL

A Cradle Song

Golden slumbers kiss your eyes,
Smiles awake you when you rise.
Sleep, pretty wantons, do not cry,
And I will sing a lullaby:
Rock them, rock them, lullaby. . . .

THOMAS DEKKER

To a Monkey

O lively, O most charming pug,
Thy graceful air, and heavenly mug;
The beauties of his mind do shine
And every bit is shaped and fine.
Your teeth are whiter than the snow,
You're a great buck, you're a great beau;
Your eyes are of so nice a shape,
More like a Christian's than an ape;
Your cheek is like the rose's bloom,
Your hair is like the raven's plume;
Your nose's cast is of the Roman.
He is a very pretty woman.
I could not get a rhyme for Roman,
So was obliged to call him woman.

MARJORIE FLEMING (1803-1811)

gripes, griffins

On a Pet Bird Killed by a Cat

When I remember again
How my Philip was slain,
Never half the pain
Was between you twain,
Pyramus and Thisbe,
As then befell to me:
I wept and I wailed,
The tears down hailed,
But nothing it availed
To call Philip again,
Whom our cat hath slain. . . .
It had a velvet cap,
And would sit upon my lap,

And seek after small worms,
And sometimes white bread-crumbs. . . .
Sometimes he would gasp
When he saw a wasp;
A fly or a gnat,
He would fly at that;
And prettily he would pant
When he saw an ant;
Lord, how he would pry
After the butterfly!
Lord, how he would hop
After the grassop!
And when I said, 'Phip, Phip!'
Then he would leap and skip,
And take me by the lip. . . .
For he would come and go,
And fly so to and fro;
And on me he would leap
When I was asleep
And his feathers shake,
Wherewith he would make
Me often for to wake.'

JOHN SKELTON

grassop, grasshopper

On the Cat that Killed the Bird

God send cats sorrow and shame!
That cat, specially,
That slew so cruelly
My little pretty sparrow
That I brought up at Carowe.
O cat of churlish kind. . . .
I would thou had'st been blind!
The leopards savage,
The lions in their rage,
Might catch thee in their paws,
And gnaw thee in their jaws!
The serpents of Lebany
Might sting thee venomously!
The dragons with their tongues
Might poison thy liver and lungs! . . .
Of Inde, the greedy gripes
Might tear out all thy tripes!
Of Arcady the bears
Might pluck away thine ears!
The wild wolf Lycaon
Bite asunder thy backbone!
Of Etna, the burning hill,
That day and night burneth still,
Set in thy tail a blaze,
That all the world may gaze
And wonder upon thee,
From Ocean (the great sea)
Unto the Isles of Orcady,
From Tilbury Ferry
To the plain of Salisbury!
So treacherously my bird to kill
That never owed thee evil will!

JOHN SKELTON

The War-horse

The glory of his nostrils is terrible.
He paweth in the valley,
And rejoiceth in his strength;
He goeth to meet the armed men.
He mocketh at fear and is not affrighted;
Neither turneth he back from the sword.
The quiver rattleth against him,
The glittering spear and the shield;
He swalloweth the ground with fierceness and rage. . . .
He smelleth the battle afar off,
The thunder of the captains,
And the shouting.

THE BIBLE

Goody Blake

Old Goody Blake was old and poor;
Ill fed she was, and thinly clad;
And any man who passed her door
Might see how poor a hut she had.

All day she spun in her poor dwelling:
And then her three hours' work at night,
Alas! 'twas hardly worth the telling,
It would not pay for candle-light.

Remote from sheltered village-green,
On a hill's northern side she dwelt,
Where from sea-blasts the hawthorns lean,
And hoary dews are slow to melt.

By the same fire to boil their pottage,
Two poor old dames, as I have known,
Will often live in one small cottage;
But she, poor woman! housed alone.

'Twas well enough, when summer came,
The long, warm, lightsome summer-day,
Then at her door the canty dame
Would sit, as any linnet, gay.

But when the ice our streams did fetter,
Oh then how her old bones would shake!
You would have said, if you had met her,
'Twas a hard time for Goody Blake.

Her evenings then were dull and dead:
Sad case it was, as you may think,
For very cold to go to bed;
And then for cold not sleep a wink.

O joy for her! whene'er in winter
The winds at night had made a rout,
And scattered many a lusty splinter
And many a rotten bough about.

Yet never had she, well or sick,
As every man who knew her says,
A pile beforehand, turf or stick,
Enough to warm her for three days.

WILLIAM WORDSWORTH

Folks

I've heard so much about other folks' folks,
How somebody's Uncle told such jokes
The cat split laughing and had to be stitched,
How somebody's Aunt got so bewitched
She fried the kettle and washed the water
And spanked a letter and posted her daughter.
Other folks' folks get so well known,
And nobody knows about my own.

TED HUGHES

A Fishing Song

There was a boy whose name was Phinn,
And he was fond of fishing;
His father could not keep him in,
Nor all his mother's wishing.

His life's ambition was to land
A fish of several pound weight;
The chief thing he could understand
Was hooks, or worms for ground-bait.

The worms crept out, the worms crept in,
From every crack and pocket;
He had a worm-box made of tin,
With proper worms to stock it.

He gave his mind to breeding worms
As much as he was able;
His sister spoke in angry terms
To see them on the table.

You found one walking up the stairs,
You found one in a bonnet,
Or, in the bed-room, unawares,
You set your foot upon it.

W. B. RANDS

Winter's Beauty

Is it not fine to walk in spring,
When leaves are born, and hear birds sing?
And when they lose their singing powers,
In summer, watch the bees at flowers?
Is it not fine, when summer's past,
To have the leaves, no longer fast,
Biting my heel where'er I go,
Or dancing lightly on my toe?
Now winter's here and rivers freeze;
As I walk out I see the trees,
Wherein the pretty squirrels sleep,
All standing in the snow so deep:
And every twig, however small,
Is blossomed white and beautiful.
Then welcome, winter, with thy power
To make this tree a big white flower;
To make this tree a lovely sight,
With fifty brown arms draped in white,
While thousands of small fingers show
In soft white gloves of purest snow.

W. H. DAVIES

The Hen and the Carp

Once in a roostery
There lived a speckled hen, and when —
Ever she laid an egg this hen
    Ecstatically cried,
'O progeny miraculous, particular spectaculous,
    What a wonderful hen am I!'

Down in a pond nearby
Perchance a fat and broody carp
Was basking, but her ears were sharp —
    She heard Dame Cackle cry:
'O progeny miraculous, particular spectaculous,
    What a wonderful hen am I!'

'Ah, Cackle,' bubbled she,
'For your single egg, O silly one,
I lay at least a million;
    Suppose for each I cried:
'O progeny miraculous, particular spectaculous!'
    What a hullabaloo there'd be!'

IAN SERRAILLIER

I'm the Boy that Builds the Boat

I'm the boy that builds the boat,
And I'm the boy that sails her!
I'm the boy that catches the fish
And takes them home to Lizer.
   Hip yer partner, Sally Tibbo,
   Hip yer partner, Sally Brown!
   Fogo, Twill-in-gate,
   Moreton's Harbour,
   All around the circle.

Flour and crumbs to cover your fish,
Cake and tea for supper,
Cod fish in the spring o' the year
Fried in rancid butter.
   Hip yer partner, Sally Tibbo . . .

I don't want your rancid fish,
That's no good for winter;
I could buy as good as that
Down in Bonavista.
   Hip yer partner, Sally Tibbo . . .

I took Lizer to a dance,
And faith, but she could travel!
Every step that she did take
Was up to her knees in gravel.
   Hip yer partner, Sally Tibbo . . .

A Kind Lady

You give your coffee to the cat,
 You stroke the dog for coming,
And all your face grows kinder at
 The little brown bee's humming.

E. B. BROWNING

Allie

Allie, call the birds in,
 The birds from the sky!
Allie calls, Allie sings,
 Down they all fly:
First there came
Two white doves,
 Then a sparrow from her nest,
Then a clucking bantam hen,
 Then a robin red-breast.

Allie, call the beasts in,
 The beasts, every one!
Allie calls, Allie sings,
 In they all run:
First there came
Two black lambs,
 Then a grunting Berkshire sow,
Then a dog without a tail,
 Then a red and white cow.

Allie, call the fish up,
　The fish from the stream!
Allie calls, Allie sings,
　Up they all swim:
First there came
Two gold fish,
　A minnow and a miller's thumb,
Then a school of little trout,
　Then the twisting eels come.

Allie, call the children,
　Call them from the green!
Allie calls, Allie sings,
　Soon they run in:
First there came
Tom and Madge,
　Kate and I who'll not forget
How we played by the water's edge
　Till the April sun set.

ROBERT GRAVES

The Prince

Sweet Peridarchus was a Prince,
The Prince he was of—Mouses;
He roved and roamed the haunts of Men,
And ranged about their houses.

He gnawed his way along a street,
Through holes in every wainscot;
Fandangoed in the attics and
From basement on to basement.

His eyes like bits of rubies shone;
His coat, as sleek as satin,
With teeth as sharp as needle-points
He kept to keep him fat in.

His squeak so sharp in the small hours rang
That every waker wondered;
He trimmed his whiskers stiff as wire,
Had sweethearts by the hundred.

He'd gut a Cheshire cheese with ease,
Plum cake devoured in slices,
Lard, haggis, suet, sausages,
And everything that nice is.

Cork out, he'd dangle down his tail
For oil that was in bottle;
Nothing too sweet, nothing too fat
For Peridarchus' throttle.

He'd dance upon a chimney-pot,
The merry stars a-twinkling;
Or, scampering up a chandelier
Set all the lustres tinkling.

He'd skip into a pianoforte
To listen how it sounded;
He bored into a butt of wine,
And so was nearly drownded.

At midnight when he sat at meat,
Twelve saucy sonsy maidens,
With bee-sweet voices ditties sang,
Some sad ones, and some gay ones.

For bodyguard he had a score
Of Warriors grim and hardy;
They raided every larder round,
From Peebles to Cromarty.

Grimalkin—deep in dreams she lay,
Comes he, with these gay friskers,
Steals up and gnaws away her claws,
And plucks out all her whiskers.

He scaled a bell-rope where there snored
The Bailiff and his Lady;
Danced on his nose, nibbled her toes,
And kissed the squalling Baby.

A merry life was his, I trow,
Despite it was a short one;
One night he met a mort of rats —
He bared his teeth, and fought one:

A bully ruffian, thrice his size;
But when the conflict ended,
He sighed, 'Alack, my back is broke,
And that can ne'er be mended.'

They laid him lifeless on a bier.
They lapped him up in ermine;
They lit a candle, inches thick,
His Uncle preached the sermon:

'O Mouseland, mourn for him that's gone,
Our noble Peridarchus!
In valiant fight but yesternight,
And now, alas, a carcass!

'A Hero — Mouse or Man — is one
Who never wails or winces;
Friend, shed a tear for him that's here,
The Princeliest of Princes!'

WALTER DE LA MARE

House Hunters

Birds will be house-hunting
Soon—think of that!
Crows in the elm-tops
And larks on the flat,
Owls in the belfry
And wren in the leaves,
And swifts will go house-hunting
Under the eaves.

Moorhen will hunt for her
House in the reeds,
Chaffinch the apple-tree
Bough ere she breeds,
Thrush in the hollow oak,
Sparrow won't care—
Here, there and everywhere,
Any old where!

Cuckoo won't trouble,
She'll just stop and call,
But starling and nightingale,
Blackbird and all,
Jays as they chatter,
And doves as they croon,
Soon will be house-hunting,
Think of it—soon!

ELEANOR FARJEON

Two Rivers

Says Tweed to Till,
'What makes you run so still?'
Says Till to Tweed,
'Though you run with speed,
And I run slow,
For one man that you drown,
I drown two.'

My Master Hath a Garden

My master hath a garden, full-filled with divers flowers,
Where thou may'st gather posies gay, all times and hours,
  Here nought is heard
  But paradise-bird,
  Harp, dulcimer, and lute,
   With cymbal,
   And timbrel,
  And the gentle sounding flute.

Oh! Jesus, Lord, my heal and weal, my bliss complete,
Make thou my heart thy garden-plot, true, fair and neat
  That I may hear
  This music clear,
  Harp, dulcimer, and lute,
   With cymbal,
   And timbrel,
  And the gentle sounding flute.

The Song of the Old Mother

I rise in the dawn, and I kneel and blow
Till the seed of the fire flicker and glow;
And then I must scrub and bake and sweep
Till stars are beginning to blink and peep;
And the young lie long and dream in their bed
Of the matching of ribbons for bosom and head,
And their day goes over in idleness,
And they sigh if the wind but lift a tress:
While I must work because I am old,
And the seed of the fire gets feeble and cold.

W. B. YEATS

The Leather-winged Bat

'I,' said the little leather-winged bat,
'I'll tell you the reason that,
The reason that I fly in the night
Is because my love's my heart's delight.'

'I,' said the woodpecker, sitting on a fence,
'Once I courted a handsome wench.
She got saucy and from me fled;
Ever since then my head's been red.'

'I,' said the blue-bird as she flew,
'If I were a young man, I'd have two;
If one got saucy and off did go,
I'd have a new string for my bow.'

The Bells

I

Pancakes and fritters,
Say the bells of St. Peter's.
Where must we fry 'em?
Say the bells of Cold Higham.
In yonder land furrow,
Say the bells of Wellingborough.
You owe me a shilling,
Say the bells of Great Billing.
When will you pay me?
Say the bells of Middleton Cheney.
When I am able,
Say the bells of Dunstable,
That will never be,
Say the bells of Coventry.
O yes it will,
Says Northampton Great Bell.

II

Three crows on a tree,
Say the bells of Oswestry.

Roast beef, and be merry,
Say the bells of Shrewsbury.

Three gold canaries,
Say the bells of St. Mary's.

A boiling pot and a stewing pan,
Say the bells of St. Julian.

You're a rogue for sartin,
Say the bells of St. Martin.

Ivy, holly, and mistletoe,
Say the bells of Wistanstow.

High Spirits

To northern seas I'll in a twinkling sail,
And mount upon the snortings of a whale
To some black cloud; thence down I'll madly sweep
On forked lightning, to the deepest deep,
Where through some sucking pool I will be hurled
With rapture to the other side of the world!

JOHN KEATS

The Fur Coat

I walked out in my Coat of Pride;
I looked about on every side;

And said the mountains should not be
Just where they were, and that the sea

Was out of place, and that the beech
Should be an oak! And then, from each

I turned in dignity, as if
They were not there! I sniffed a sniff;

And climbed upon my sunny shelf;
And sneezed a while; and scratched myself.

JAMES STEPHENS

35

The Mermaid

Who would be
A mermaid fair,
Singing alone,
Combing her hair
Under the sea,
In a golden curl
With a comb of pearl
On a throne?

I would be a mermaid fair;
I would sing to myself the whole of the day;
With a comb of pearl I would comb my hair;
And still as I combed I would sing and say,
'Who is it loves me? who loves not me?'
I would comb my hair till my ringlets would fall,
  Low adown, low adown,
From under my starry sea-bud crown
Low adown and around,
And I should look like a fountain of gold. . . .
And if I should carol aloud, from aloft
All things that are forked, and horned, and soft,
Would lean out from the hollow sphere of the sea,
All looking down for the love of me.

ALFRED TENNYSON

Ploughing on Sunday

The white cock's tail
Tosses in the wind.
The turkey-cock's tail
Glitters in the sun.

Water in the fields.
The wind pours down.
The feathers flare
And bluster in the wind.

Remus, blow your horn!
I'm ploughing on Sunday,
Ploughing North America.
Blow your horn!

Tum-ti-tum,
Ti-tum-tum-tum!
The turkey-cock's tail
Spreads to the sun.

The white cock's tail
Streams to the moon.
Water in the fields.
The wind pours down.

WALLACE STEVENS

Peter to Tea

A glimpse of a pram through the window;
A whistle from Auntie Bee;
A rat-tat-tat at the letter-box,
And the cousins are here to tea;
Marion is bald, as babies are;
Peter has short red hair;
Mother takes charge of Marion,
But Peter falls to my share.

So out come the bricks from the cupboard,
And Peter breathes loud through his nose,
And clasps me lovingly round his neck
While I try to build him a house:
A line of bricks for the garden-wall;
Two bricks for the chimney-pot;
Then a moment's pause . . . till Peter
Flops forward and smashes the lot!

Another game he plays is,
When Mother isn't about,
He drags me along to the front door
And begs me to lock him out;
But no sooner's the door shut on him
Than he bangs till I let him in;
Then he cries 'Do you want any taters, ma'am?'
And grins a most rascally grin.

Now the bricks go back to the cupboard,
And we settle down to our teas;
And I'll tell you something peculiar:
Peter likes jam with his cheese;
But before the meal's half over
He squirms for his mother's lap,
Or crawls round the legs of the table,
Till he gets what he wants—a good slap.

Tempest and temper! But not for long,
For life's too busy to cry;
So Peter and I have a wrestling-match
Till it's time to kiss good-bye;
And Peter is rolled away at last
On the handles-end of the pram,
His face beaming, his little ginger
Hair all sticky with jam.

And what's left? An enormous silence—
A house empty and still;
A sinkful of dirty cups and plates
Piled up in a huge hill;
Three bricks pushed under the carpet,
Three kicks on the painted door,
And a handful of soft-chewed crusts
That Peter has thrown on the floor!

JOHN WALSH

Nest Eggs

Birds all the sunny day
  Flutter and quarrel
Here in the arbour-like
  Tent of the laurel.

Here in the fork
  The brown nest is seated;
Four little blue eggs
  The mother keeps heated.

While we stand watching her,
  Staring like gabies,
Safe in each egg are the
  Bird's little babies.

Soon the frail eggs they shall
  Chip, and upspringing
Make all the April woods
  Merry with singing.

Younger than we are,
  O children, and frailer,
Soon in blue air they'll be,
  Singer and sailor.

We, so much older,
  Taller and stronger,
We shall look down on the
  Birds no longer.

They shall go flying
  With musical speeches
High overhead in the
  Tops of the beeches.

In spite of our wisdom
  And sensible talking,
We on our feet must go
  Plodding and walking.

R. L. STEVENSON

Gaps

Kate went to sleep in starlit quiet
  And woke in rattling thunder,
But what had happened in between?
  All she can do is wonder.

Kim dozed in Surrey countryside
  And this is Waterloo;
And has he snored for thirty miles?
  That's what he'll never know.

The bramble was a wilderness,
  The acorn was an oak,
The young were old, the old were dead
  When Rip Van Winkle woke.

RAYMOND O'MALLEY

Past Three O'Clock

Past three o'clock
And a cold frosty morning;
Past three o'clock;
Good morrow masters all!

Born is a Baby,
Gentle as may be,
Son of the eternal
Father supernal.
    Past three o'clock
    And a cold frosty morning;
    Past three o'clock;
    Good morrow masters all!

Seraph choir singeth,
Angel bell ringeth:
Hark how they rhyme it,
Time it, and chime it.
    Past three o'clock
    And a cold frosty morning;
    Past three o'clock;
    Good morrow masters all!

Cheese from the dairy
Bring they for Mary,
And, not for money,
Butter and honey.
    Past three o'clock
    And a cold frosty morning;
    Past three o'clock;
    Good morrow masters all!

Light out of star-land
Leadeth from far land
Princes to meet him.
Worship and greet him.
  Past three o'clock
  And a cold frosty morning;
  Past three o'clock;
  Good morrow masters all!

The Eve of St. Agnes

St. Agnes' Eve—Ah, bitter chill it was!
  The owl, for all his feathers, was a-cold;
The hare limped trembling through the frozen grass,
  And silent was the flock in woolly fold:
  Numb were the Beadsman's fingers, while he told
    His rosary, and while his frosted breath,
  Like pious incense from a censer old,
    Seemed taking flight for heaven, without a death,
Past the sweet Virgin's picture, while his prayer he saith.

JOHN KEATS

The Owl

Sweet Suffolk owl, so trimly dight
With feathers, like a lady bright,
Thou sing'st alone, sitting by night,
   Te whit, te whoo!
Thy note that forth so freely rolls,
With shrill command the mouse controls,
And sings a dirge for dying souls,
   Te whit, te whoo!

T. VAUTOR

dirge, song in memory of the dead

Kittens and Chickens

That is the Kitten,
The one in black
That you see at the back,
Whose heart was smitten
To eat a chicken,
And made a picking
Of the chicken's bones
Out there, on the stones.
When the feast was ended,
And the undefended
Fowl just swallowed,

The Hen came, followed
By half the flock
And—oh!—the Cock!
He stuck out his chest,
And set up his crest,
And crowed defiance
Like an army of lions.
The Kitten stood there
With his tail in the air,
Then took his departure
Like the arrow of an archer
Swift from a bow,
And left the Cock
As firm as a rock,
To ruffle and crow.
In a corner was sitting
Another Kitten,
White, not black,
Who heard the clack,
And knowing the story
Of the chicken gory
Had trepidations
And meditations
About taking chickens,
And such, for pickings.
But cats will be cats
The whole world long!

W. B. RANDS

If I Should Ever by Chance

If I should ever by chance grow rich
I'll buy Codham, Cockridden, and Childerditch,
Roses, Pyrgo, and Lapwater,
And let them all to my elder daughter.
The rent I shall ask of her will be only
Each year's first violets, white and lonely,
The first primroses and orchises —
She must find them before I do, that is.
But if she finds a blossom on furze
Without rent they shall all for ever be hers,
Whenever I am sufficiently rich:
Codham, Cockridden and Childerditch,
Roses, Pyrgo and Lapwater —
I shall give them all to my elder daughter.

EDWARD THOMAS

Earth's Motion

When we are going in a train
At sixty miles an hour,
We marvel at the mighty speed,
And at the engine's power.

But Earth is moving faster far,
Just like a spinning top,
All through the day, all through the night,
Without a single stop.

And as she turns herself about,
She circles round the sun,
At sixty thousand miles an hour,
Her journey never done.

Only so softly does she turn,
Without a jolt or spill,
It took a clever man to find
She wasn't standing still.

E. L. M. KING

Midnight

Midnight was come, when every living thing
    With sweet, sound sleep their weary limbs did rest,
The beasts were still, the little birds that sing
    Now sweetly slept beside their mother's breast.

The ugly bear now minded not the stake,
    Nor how the cruel mastiffs do him tear,
The stag lay still unroused from the brake,
    The foamy boar feared not the hunter's spear.

The golden stars were whirled amid their race,
    And on the earth did laugh with twinkling light,
When each thing, nestled in his resting-place,
    Forgot the day's pain with pleasure of the night.

THOMAS SACKVILLE

The Kitten and the Falling Leaves

See the kitten on the wall,
Sporting with the leaves that fall,
Withered leaves—one—two—and three—
From the lofty elder tree!
Through the calm and frosty air
Of this morning bright and fair. . . .
But the Kitten, how she starts,
Crouches, stretches, paws, and darts!
First at one, and then its fellow,
Just as light and just as yellow;
There are many now—now one—
Now they stop and there are none:
What intenseness of desire
In her upward eye of fire,
With a tiger-leap half-way
Now she meets the coming prey,
Lets it go as fast, and then
Has it in her power again:
Now she works with three or four,
Like an Indian conjuror;
Quick as he in feats of art,
Far beyond in joy of heart. . . .

WILLIAM WORDSWORTH

The Bat

Myself, I rather like the bat,
It's not a mouse, it's not a rat.
It has no feathers, yet has wings,
It's quite inaudible when it sings.
It zigzags through the evening air
And never lands on ladies' hair,
A fact of which men spend their lives
Attempting to convince their wives.

OGDEN NASH

A Willow-pattern Dish is Broken

They gather flowers of every hue,
  And fish in boats for fishes,
Build summer-houses painted blue,
  But life's as frail as dishes.

Walking about their groves of trees,
  Blue bridges and blue rivers,
How little thought those two Chinese
  They'd both be smashed to shivers.

THOMAS HOOD

Cows

Half the time they munched the grass, and all the time they lay
Down in the water-meadows, the lazy month of May,
      A-chewing,
      A-mooing,
   To pass the hours away.

  'Nice weather,' said the brown cow.
  'Ah,' said the white.
  'Grass is very tasty.'
  'Grass is all right.'

Half the time they munched the grass, and all the time they lay
Down in the water-meadows, the lazy month of May,
      A-chewing,
      A-mooing,
   To pass the hours away.

  'Rain coming,' said the brown cow.
  'Ah,' said the white.
  'Flies is very tiresome.'
  'Flies bite.'

Half the time they munched the grass, and all the time they lay
Down in the water-meadows, the lazy month of May,
      A-chewing,
      A-mooing,
    To pass the hours away.

'Time to go,' said the brown cow.
'Ah,' said the white.
'Nice chat.' 'Very pleasant.'
'Night.' 'Night.'

Half the time they munched the grass, and all the time they lay
Down in the water-meadows, the lazy month of May,
      A-chewing,
      A-mooing,
    To pass the hours away.

JAMES REEVES

The Walrus and the Carpenter

The sun was shining on the sea,
　Shining with all his might:
He did his very best to make
　The billows smooth and bright—
And this was odd, because it was
　The middle of the night.

The moon was shining sulkily,
　Because she thought the sun
Had got no business to be there
　After the day was done—
'It's very rude of him,' she said,
　'To come and spoil the fun!'

The sea was wet as wet could be,
　The sands were dry as dry.
You could not see a cloud, because
　No cloud was in the sky:
No birds were flying overhead—
　There were no birds to fly.

The Walrus and the Carpenter
  Were walking hand in hand;
They wept like anything to see
  Such quantities of sand:
'If this were only cleared away,'
  They said, 'it *would* be grand!'

'If seven maids with seven mops
  Swept it for half a year,
Do you suppose,' the Walrus said,
  'That they could get it clear?'
'I doubt it,' said the Carpenter,
  And shed a bitter tear.

'O Oysters, come and walk with us!'
  The Walrus did beseech.
'A pleasant walk, a pleasant talk,
  Along the briny beach:
We cannot do with more than four,
  To give a hand to each.'

The eldest Oyster looked at him,
  But never a word he said:
The eldest Oyster winked his eye,
  And shook his heavy head—
Meaning to say he did not choose
  To leave the oyster-bed.

But four young Oysters hurried up,
  All eager for the treat:
Their coats were brushed, their faces washed,
  Their shoes were clean and neat —
And this was odd, because, you know,
  They hadn't any feet.

Four other Oysters followed them,
  And yet another four;
And thick and fast they came at last,
  And more, and more, and more —
All hopping through the frothy waves,
  And scrambling to the shore.

The Walrus and the Carpenter
  Walked on a mile or so,
And then they rested on a rock
  Conveniently low:
And all the little Oysters stood
  And waited in a row.

'The time has come,' the Walrus said,
  'To talk of many things:
Of shoes — and ships — and sealing-wax —
  Of cabbages — and kings —
And why the sea is boiling hot —
  And whether pigs have wings.'

'But, wait a bit,' the Oysters cried,
    'Before we have our chat;
For some of us are out of breath,
    And all of us are fat!'
'No hurry!' said the Carpenter.
    They thanked him much for that.

'A loaf of bread,' the Walrus said,
    'Is what we chiefly need:
Pepper and vinegar besides
    Are very good indeed —
Now if you're ready, Oysters dear,
    We can begin to feed.'

'But not on us!' the Oysters cried
    Turning a little blue.
'After such kindness, that would be
    A dismal thing to do!'
'The night is fine,' the Walrus said.
    'Do you admire the view?'

'It was so nice of you to come!
    And you are very nice!'
The Carpenter said nothing but
    'Cut me another slice:
I wish you were not quite so deaf —
    I've had to ask you twice!'

'It seems a shame,' the Walrus said,
  'To play them such a trick,
After we've brought them out so far,
  And made them trot so quick!'
The Carpenter said nothing but
  'The butter's spread too thick!'

'I weep for you,' the Walrus said:
  'I deeply sympathize.'
With sobs and tears he sorted out
  Those of the largest size,
Holding his pocket-handkerchief
  Before his streaming eyes.

'O Oysters,' said the Carpenter,
  'You've had a pleasant run!
Shall we be trotting home again?'
  But answer came there none—
And this was scarcely odd, because
  They'd eaten every one.

LEWIS CARROLL

56

Fireside Dreams in Winter

. . . The soundless earth is muffled
And the caked earth is shuffled. . . .
And in the same moment—hark!
'Tis the early April lark,
Or the rooks, with busy caw,
Foraging for sticks and straw.
Thou shalt, at one glance, behold
The daisy and the marigold. . . .
Thou shalt see the field-mouse peep
Meagre from its celled sleep;
And the snake, all winter-thin,
Cast on sunny bank its skin;
Freckled nest-eggs thou shalt see
Hatching in the hawthorn-tree,
When the hen-bird's wing doth rest
Quiet on her mossy nest;
Then the hurry and alarm
When the bee-hive casts its swarm;
Acorns ripe down-pattering,
While the autumn breezes sing. . . .

JOHN KEATS

Praise of a Horse

When I bestride him, I soar, I am a hawk;
He trots the air.
The earth sings when he touches it;
The basest horn of his hoof is more musical
Than the pipe of Hermes.
He's of the colour of the nutmeg
And of the heat of the ginger.
He is a beast for Perseus.

WILLIAM SHAKESPEARE

Clock-a-Clay

In the cow-slip pips I lie,
Hidden from the buzzing fly,
While green grass beneath me lies,
Pearled with dew like fishes' eyes,
Here I lie, a clock-a-clay,
Waiting for the time of day.

While grassy forest quakes surprise,
And the wild wind sobs and sighs,
My gold home rocks as like to fall
On its pillar green and tall;
When the pattering rain drives by
Clock-a-clay keeps warm and dry.

Day by day and night by night,
All the week I hide from sight;
In the cow-slip pips I lie,
In rain and dew still warm and dry;
Day and night, and night and day,
Red, black-spotted clock-a-clay.

My home shakes in wind and showers,
Pale green pillar topped with flowers,
Bending at the wild wind's breath,
Till I touch the grass beneath;
Here I live, lone clock-a-clay,
Watching for the time of day.

JOHN CLARE

clock-a-clay, lady-bird

Sight

By the lamplit stall I loitered, feasting my eyes
On colours ripe and rich for the heart's desire —
Tomatoes redder than Krakatoa's fire,
Oranges like old sunsets over Tyre,
And apples golden-green as the glades of Paradise.

And as I lingered lost in divine delight,
My heart thanked God for the goodly gift of sight
And all youth's lively senses keen and quick . . .
When suddenly behind me in the night
I heard the tapping of a blind man's stick.

WILFRID GIBSON

The Boy and His Top

A little boy had bought a top,
The best in all the toyman's shop;
He made a whip with good eel's skin,
He lashed the top and made it spin;
All the children within call,
And the servants, one and all,
Stood round to see it and admire.
At last the top began to tire;
He cried out, 'Pray, don't whip me, master,
You whip too hard; I can't spin faster;
I can spin quite as well without it.'
The little boy replied, 'I doubt it!'

J. H. FRERE

On a Cat Ageing

He blinks upon the hearth-rug
And yawns in deep content,
Accepting all the comforts
That Providence has sent.

Louder he purrs, and louder,
In one glad hymn of praise
For all the night's adventures,
For quiet, restful days.

Life will go on for ever,
With all that cat can wish:
Warmth and the glad procession
Of fish and milk and fish.

Only — the thought disturbs him —
He's noticed once or twice,
The times are somehow breeding
A nimbler race of mice.

ALEXANDER GRAY

The Cow

There Once was a Cow with a Double Udder.
When I think of it now, I just have to shudder!
She was too much for One, you can bet your Life:
She had to be Milked by a Man and his Wife.

THEODORE ROETHKE

Evening Shadows

The shadows now so long do grow,
That brambles like tall cedars show;
Molehills seem mountains, and the ant
Appears a monstrous elephant.

CHARLES COTTON

Seumas Beg

A man was sitting underneath a tree
Outside a village, and he asked me what
Name was upon this place, and said that he
Was never there before. He told a lot
Of stories to me too. His nose was flat.
I asked him how it happened, and he said
The first mate of the *Mary Anne* done that
With a marling spike one day, but he was dead,
And jolly good job too; and he'd have gone
A long way to have killed him, and he had
A gold ring in one ear; the other one
'Was bit off by a crocodile, bedad.'
That's what he said. He taught me how to chew.
He was a real nice man. He liked me too.

JAMES STEPHENS

Seumas Beg, Little James

The Wind

The wind begun to knead the grass
As women do a dough;
He flung a handful at the plain,
A handful at the sky.
The leaves unhooked themselves from trees
And started all abroad;
The dust did scoop itself like hands
And throw away the road.
The wagons quickened on the street;
The thunders gossiped low;
The lightning showed a yellow head
And then a livid toe.
The birds put up the bars to nests;
The cattle flung to barns.
Then came one drop of giant rain;
And then, as if the hands
That held the dams had parted hold,
The waters wrecked the sky,
But overlooked my father's house,
Just quartering a tree.

EMILY DICKINSON

5

The Flint

An emerald is green as grass,
   A ruby red as blood,
A sapphire shines as blue as heaven;
   But a flint lies in the mud.

A diamond is a brilliant stone
   To catch the world's desire;
An opal holds a rainbow light,
   But a flint holds fire.

CHRISTINA ROSSETTI

Four Dates

William the Conqueror, ten sixty-six,
Played on the Saxons oft-cruel tricks.

Columbus sailed the ocean blue,
In fourteen hundred and ninety-two.

The Spanish Armada met its fate,
In fifteen hundred and eighty-eight.

In sixteen hundred and sixty-six,
London burnt like rotten sticks.

Kingcups in Town

Down the street the old man came,
And on his head he bore a flame.

I stopped to gaze, so he stopped too.
'Want some?' he said. 'Indeed I do.

Where did you get them?' 'Uxbridge way,
All the lot fresh-picked today

Off the island there,' he said,
Shifting the basket from his head.

'You gets 'em when the water's out,
O' course. I had to wait about

All night for 'em. The bud'll bloom
Lovely when they're in your room.'

I took the bunch from him, still wet,
And then the kingcup-gatherer set

His brimming basket on his old
Grey head, and walked beneath the gold,

Yes, walked off in his broken boots,
And the shabbiest of suits,

Crowned in the may-time of the spring,
More gloriously than a king.

ELEANOR FARJEON

The Bells

Hear the sledges with the bells—
  Silver bells!
How they tinkle, tinkle, tinkle
  In the icy air of night!
All the heavens seem to twinkle
  With a crystalline delight:
Hear the jingling and the tinkling of the bells.

Hear the mellow wedding bells,
  Golden bells!
Through the balmy air of night,
How they ring out their delight:
Hear the rhyming and the chiming of the bells.

Hear the loud alarum bells—
  Brazen bells!
In the startled ear of night
How they scream out their affright!
Too much horrified to speak,
They can only shriek, shriek:
Hear the clamour and the clangour of the bells!

Hear the tolling of the bells—
  Iron bells!
In the silence of the night,
How we shiver with affright
Hear the moaning and the groaning of the bells.

EDGAR ALLAN POE

Puck's Song

Now the hungry lion roars,
  And the wolf behowls the moon;
Whilst the heavy ploughman snores,
  All with weary task fordone.

Now the wasted brands do glow,
  Whilst the screech-owl, screeching loud,
Puts the wretch that lies in woe
  In remembrance of a shroud.

Now it is the time of night
  That the graves, all gaping wide,
Every one lets forth his sprite,
  In the churchway paths to glide;

And we fairies, that do run
  By the triple Hecate's team
From the presence of the sun,
  Following darkness like a dream,

Now are frolic: not a mouse
Shall disturb this hallowed house.
I am sent, with broom, before,
To sweep the dust behind the door.

WILLIAM SHAKESPEARE

shroud, a wrapping for dead people

The King of the Crocodiles

'Oh, I have lost my darling boy,
In whom my soul had all its joy;
He stooped by the river down to drink,
And there was a Crocodile by the brink.

'He did not venture in to swim,
He only stooped to drink at the brim;
But under the reeds the Crocodile lay,
And struck with his tail and swept him away.

'Now take me in your boat, I pray,
For down the river lies my way,
And me to the Reed Island bring,
For I will go to the Crocodile King.

'He reigns not now in Crocodilople,
Proud as the Turk at Constantinople;
No ruins of his great city remain;
The Island of Reeds is his whole domain.

'Like a dervish there he passes his days,
Turns up his eyes, and fasts and prays;
And being grown pious and meek and mild,
He now never eats man, woman or child.

'The King of the Crocodiles never does wrong,
He has no tail so stiff and strong,
He has no tail to strike and slay,
But he has ears to hear what I say.'

The man replied, 'No, woman, no;
To the Island of Reeds I will not go;
I would not for any worldly thing
See the face of the Crocodile King.'

The woman she leaped into the boat,
And down the river alone did float,
And fast with the stream the boat proceeds,
And now she is come to the Island of Reeds.

The King of the Crocodiles there was seen;
He sat upon the eggs of the Queen,
And all around, a numerous rout,
The young Prince Crocodiles crawled about.

She fell upon her bended knee,
And said, 'O King, have pity on me;
Let me have vengeance for my boy,
The only thing that can give me joy.

'I know that you, sire, never do wrong,
You have no tail so stiff and strong,
You have no tail to strike and slay,
But you have ears to hear what I say.'

'You have done well,' the King replies,
And fixed on her his little eyes;
'Good woman, yes, you have done right,
But you have not described me quite.

'I have no tail to strike and slay,
And I have ears to hear what you say;
I have teeth, moreover, as you may see,
AND I WILL MAKE A MEAL OF THEE.'

Wicked the word, and bootless the boast,
As cruel King Crocodile found to his cost.
And proper reward of tyrannical might;
He showed his teeth, but he missed his bite.

'A meal of me!' the woman cried,
Taking wit in her anger, and courage beside;
She took him his forelegs and hind between,
And trundled him off the eggs of the Queen.

Two Crocodile Princes, as they played on the sand,
She caught, and grasping them one in each hand,
Thrust the head of one into the throat of the other,
And made each Crocodile Prince choke his brother.

And when she had trussed three couple this way,
She carried them off and hastened away;
And plying her oars with might and main,
Crossed the river and got to the shore again.

'Mash-Allah!' her neighbours exclaimed in delight,
She gave them a funeral supper that night,
Where they all agreed that revenge was sweet,
And young Crocodile Princes delicate meat.

ROBERT SOUTHEY

A Warning

Three children sliding on the ice
    Upon a summer's day,
It so fell out they all fell in,
    The rest they ran away.

Now had these children been at home,
    Or sliding on dry ground,
Ten thousand pounds to one penny
    They had not all been drowned.

You parents all that children have,
    And you that have got none,
If you would have them safe abroad,
    Pray keep them safe at home.

abroad, out of doors

Hunting Song

Up, up! ye dames, and lasses gay!
To the meadows trip away.
'Tis you must tend the flocks this morn,
And scare the small birds from the corn.

    Not a soul at home may stay:
      For the shepherds must go
      With lance and bow
    To hunt the wolf in the woods to-day.

Leave the hearth and leave the house
To the cricket and the mouse:
Find grannam out a sunny seat,
With babe and lambkin at her feet.

Not a soul at home must stay:
For the shepherds must go
With lance and bow
To hunt the wolf in the woods to-day.

S. T. COLERIDGE

The Snare

I hear a sudden cry of pain!
There is a rabbit in a snare:
Now I hear the cry again,
But I cannot tell from where.

But I cannot tell from where
He is calling out for aid;
Crying on the frightened air,
Making everything afraid.

Making everything afraid,
Wrinkling up his little face,
As he cries again for aid;
And I cannot find the place!

And I cannot find the place
Where his paw is in the snare:
Little one! Oh, little one!
I am searching everywhere.

JAMES STEPHENS

Goldfinches

Sometimes goldfinches one by one will drop
From low hung branches; little space they stop;
But sip and twitter, and their feathers sleek;
Then off at once, as in a wanton freak;
Or, perhaps, to show their black and golden wings,
Pausing upon their flutterings.

JOHN KEATS

How many miles to Mylor

How many miles to Mylor
  By frost and candle-light:
How long before I arrive there,
  This mild December night?

As I mounted the hill to Mylor
  Through the thick woods of Carclew,
A clock struck the three-quarters,
  And suddenly a cock crew.

At the cross-roads on the hill-top
  The snow lay on the ground,
In the quick air and the stillness,
  No movement and no sound.

'Who is it?' said a voice from the bushes
  Beneath the rowan-tree;
'Who is it?' my mouth re-echoed,
  My heart went out of me.

I cannot tell what queerness
    There lay around Carclew:
Nor whatever stirred in the hedges
    When an owl replied 'Who-whoo?'

A lamp in a lone cottage,
    A face in a window-frame,
Above the snow a wicket:
    A house without a name.

How many miles to Mylor
    This dark December night:
And shall I ever arrive there
    By frost or candle-light?

A. L. ROWSE

'Geography'

Long-legged Italy
Kicked poor Sicily
Right in the middle of the Mediterranean Sea.
Austria was Hungary,
Took a bit of Turkey,
Dipped it in Greece,
Fried it in Japan
And ate it off China.

The Old Wife and the Ghost

There was an old wife and she lived all alone
    In a cottage not far from Hitchin:
And one bright night, by the full moon light,
    Comes a ghost right into her kitchen.

About that kitchen neat and clean
    The ghost goes pottering round.
But the poor old wife is deaf as a boot
    And so hears never a sound.

The ghost blows up the kitchen fire,
    As bold as bold can be;
He helps himself from the larder shelf,
    But never a sound hears she.

He blows on his hands to make them warm,
    And whistles aloud 'Whee-hee!'
But still as a sack the old soul lies
    And never a sound hears she.

From corner to corner he runs about,
    And into the cupboard he peeps;
He rattles the door and bumps on the floor,
    But still the old wife sleeps.

Jangle and bang go the pots and pans,
    As he throws them all around;
And the plates and mugs and dishes and jugs,
    He flings them all to the ground.

Madly the ghost tears up and down
And screams like a storm at sea;
And at last the old wife stirs in her bed—
And it's 'Drat those mice,' says she.

Then the first cock crows and morning shows
And the troublesome ghost's away.
But Oh! what a pickle the poor wife sees
When she gets up next day.

'Them's tidy big mice,' the old wife thinks,
And off she goes to Hitchin,
And a tidy big cat she fetches back
To keep the mice from her kitchen.

JAMES REEVES

The Egg

Let's think of eggs.
They have no legs.
Chickens come from eggs
But they have legs.
The plot thickens:
Eggs come from chickens,
But have no legs under 'em.
What a conundrum!

OGDEN NASH

Trees

Of all the trees in England
   Her sweet three corners in,
Only the Ash, the bonnie Ash
   Burns fierce while it is green.

Of all the trees in England,
   From sea to sea again,
The Willow loveliest stoops her boughs
   Beneath the driving rain.

Of all the trees in England,
   Past frankincense and myrrh,
There's none for smell, of bloom and smoke,
   Like Lime and Juniper.

Of all the trees in England,
   Oak, Elder, Elm and Thorn,
The Yew alone burns lamps of peace
   For them that lie forlorn.

WALTER DE LA MARE

I'll go and be a Soldier

Oh why the deuce should I repine,
   And be an ill foreboder?
I'm twenty-three, and five feet nine,
   I'll go and be a soldier!

I got some gear with mickle care,
   I held it well together;
But now it's gone, and something more—
   I'll go and be a soldier!

ROBERT BURNS

mickle care, great trouble

76

The Lamb

Little Lamb, who made thee?
　Dost thou know who made thee?
Gave thee life, and bid thee feed,
By the stream and o'er the mead;
Gave thee clothing of delight,
Softest clothing, woolly, bright;
Gave thee such a tender voice,
Making all the vales rejoice?
　Little Lamb, who made thee?
　Dost thou know who made thee?

Little Lamb, I'll tell thee,
　Little Lamb, I'll tell thee:
He is calléd by thy name,
For he calls Himself a Lamb.
He is meek, and He is mild;
He became a little child.
I a child, and thou a lamb,
We are calléd by His name.
　Little Lamb, God bless thee!
　Little Lamb, God bless thee!

WILLIAM BLAKE

Get up and bar the door

It fell about the Martinmas time,
   And a gay time it was then,
When our goodwife got puddings to make,
   And she's boiled them in the pan.

The wind so cold blew south and north,
   And blew into the floor;
Quoth our goodman to our goodwife,
   'Go out and bar the door.' —

'My head is in my hussyfscap,
   Goodman, as you may see;
If it shouldn't be barred this hundred year,
   It'll not be barred by me.'

They made a paction between them two,
   They made it firm and sure,
That the first word whoever should speak
   Should rise and bar the door.

Then by there came two gentlemen,
   At twelve o'clock at night,
And they could neither see house nor hall,
   Nor coal nor candle-light.

'Now whether is this a rich man's house,
   Or whether is it a poor?'
But never a word would man or wife speak,
   For barring of the door.

And first they ate the white puddings,
  And then they ate the black;
Though muckle thought the goodwife to herself
  Yet never a word she spake.

Then said the one unto the other,
  'Here man, take ye my knife;
Do you shave off the old man's beard,
  And I'll kiss the goodwife.' —

'But there's no water in the house,
  And what shall we do then?' —
'What ails ye at the pudding-broo,
  That's boiling in the pan?'

O up then started our goodman,
  An angry man was he:
'Will ye kiss my wife before my eyes,
  And scald me with pudding-bree?'

Then up and started our goodwife,
  Gave three steps on the floor:
'Goodman, you've spoken the foremost word!
  Get up and bar the door.'

muckle, much

A Child's Dream

I had a little dog and my dog was very small:
He licked me in the face and he answered to my call:
Of all the treasures that were mine, I loved him best of all.

His nose was fresh as morning dew and blacker than the
    night:
I thought that it could even snuff the shadows and the light:
And his tail he held bravely, like a banner in a fight.

His body, covered thick with hair, was very good to smell:
His little stomach underneath was pink as any shell;
And I loved him and honoured him, more than words can tell.

We ran out in the morning, both of us, to play,
Up and down across the fields for all the sunny day;
But he ran so swiftly—he ran right away.

I looked for him, I called him entreatingly. Alas,
The dandelions would not speak, though they had seen him
    pass.
And nowhere was his waving tail among the waving grass.

I called him in a thousand ways and yet he did not come:
The pathways and the ledges were horrible and dumb.
I prayed to God, who never heard. My desperate soul
    grew numb.

The sun sank low. I ran; I prayed: 'If God has not the
    power
To find him, let me die! I cannot bear another hour.'
When suddenly I came upon a great yellow flower.

And all among its petals, such was Heaven's grace,
In that golden hour, in that golden place,
All among its petals, was his hairy face.

FRANCES CORNFORD

The Vowels

We are very little creatures,
All of different voice and features;
One of us in glAss is set,
One of us you'll find in jEt,
T'other you may see in tIn,
And the fourth a bOx within.
If the fifth you should pursue,
It can never fly from yoU.

JONATHAN SWIFT

Two Winter Joys

Frost flowers on the window-pane
Pictures in the fire —
These are two enchanting things
Of which I never tire.

Snowy palm and butterfly,
Fern and star and rose
Wake me up in Paradise
In spite of tingling toes.

Ogres, castles, dragons, dwarfs,
Black and blue and red —
Fiery wild adventures send
Me glowing up to bed.

E. L. M. KING

The Fallow Deer at the Lonely House

One without looks in tonight
Through the curtain-chink
From the sheet of glistening white;
One without looks in tonight
As we sit and think
By the fender-brink.

We do not discern those eyes
Watching in the snow;
Lit by lamps of rosy dyes
We do not discern those eyes
Wondering, aglow,
Fourfooted, tiptoe.

THOMAS HARDY

The Wee Cooper o' Fife

There was a wee cooper who lived in Fife,
   Nickity, nackity, noo, noo, noo,
And he has gotten a gentle wife.
   Hey Willie Wallacky, how John Dougall,
   Alane, quo' Rushety, roue, roue, roue.

She wadna bake, nor she wadna brew,
For the spoiling o' her comely hue.

She wadna card, nor she wadna spin,
For the shaming o' her gentle kin.

She wadna wash, nor she wadna wring,
For the spoiling o' her golden ring.

The cooper's awa to his wool-pack,
And has laid a sheep-skin on his wife's back

'It's I'll no' thrash ye, for your proud kin,
But I will thrash me ain sheep-skin.'

'Oh, I will bake, and I will brew,
And never mair think on my comely hue.

'Oh, I will card, and I will spin,
And never mair think on my gentle kin.

'Oh, I will wash, and I will wring,
And never think mair on my golden ring.'

All ye who have gotten a gentle wife
Send ye for the wee cooper of Fife.

The Lamb and the Dove

Did any bird come flying
    After Adam and Eve,
When the door was shut against them
    And they sat down to grieve?

I think not Eve's peacock
    Splendid to see,
And I think not Adam's eagle
    But a dove may be.

Did any beast come pushing
    Through the thorny hedge
Into the thorny thistle world,
    Out from Eden's edge?

I think not a lion,
    Though his strength is such;
But an innocent loving lamb
    May have done as much.

If the dove preached from her bough,
    And the lamb from his sod,
The lamb and the dove
    Were preachers sent from God.

CHRISTINA ROSSETTI

The Lincolnshire Poacher

When I was bound apprentice in famous Lincolnshire,
Full well I served my master for more than seven year,
Till I took up to poaching,
As you shall quickly hear:
    Oh, 'tis my delight on a shining night,
    In the season of the year.

As me and my companions were setting of a snare,
'Twas then we spied the game-keeper, for him we did not care,
For we can wrestle and fight, my boys,
And jump out anywhere. . . .

As me and my companions were setting four or five,
And, taking on 'em up again, we caught a hare alive,
We took the hare alive, my boys,
And through the woods did steer. . . .

I threw him on my shoulder, and then we trudged home,
We took him to a neighbour's house and sold him for a crown,
We sold him for a crown, my boys,
But I will not tell you where. . . .

Success to every gentleman that lives in Lincolnshire,
Success to every poacher that wants to sell a hare,
Bad luck to every game-keeper
That will not sell his deer:
    Oh, 'tis my delight on a shining night,
    In the season of the year.

French and English

Never go to France
    Unless you know the lingo.
If you do, like me,
    You will repent, by jingo.

Signs I had to make
    For every little notion,
Limbs all going like
    A telegraph in motion.

For wine I reeled about,
    To show my meaning fully,
And made a pair of horns
    To ask for beef and bully.

If I wanted bread
    My jaws I'd set a-going,
And asked for new-laid eggs
    By clapping hands and crowing.

If I wished a ride,
    I'll tell you how I got it:
On my stick astride,
    I made believe to trot it.

Never go to France
    Unless you know the lingo.
If you do, like me,
    You will repent, by jingo.

THOMAS HOOD

Signs of Rain

The hollow winds begin to blow,
The clouds look black, the glass is low,
The soot falls down, the spaniels sleep,
The spiders from their cobwebs peep:
Last night the sun went pale to bed,
The moon in halos hid her head.
The walls are damp, the ditches smell,
Closed is the pink-eyed pimpernel.
Hark how the chairs and tables crack!
Old Betty's joints are on the rack.
Puss on the hearth, with velvet paws,
Sits wiping o'er her whiskered jaws.
At dusk the squalid toad was seen,
Hopping and crawling o'er the green.
My dog, so altered in his taste,
Quits mutton-bones on grass to feast.
'Twill surely rain, I see with sorrow,
Our jaunt must be put off tomorrow.

E. JENNER

A Tulip

She slept beneath a tree
Remembered but by me.
I touched her cradle mute;
She recognized the foot,
Put on her carmine suit —
    And see!

EMILY DICKINSON

William I — 1066

William the First was the first of our kings,
Not counting Ethelreds, Egberts and things,
And he had himself crowned and anointed and blest
In Ten-Sixty-I-Needn't-Tell-You-The-Rest.

But being a Norman, King William the first
By the Saxons he conquered was hated and cursed,
And they planned and they plotted far into the night,
Which William could tell by the candles alight.

Then William decided these rebels to quell
By ringing the Curfew, a sort of bell,
And if any Saxon was found out of bed
After eight o'clock sharp, it was Off With His Head!

So at BONG NUMBER ONE they all started to run
Like a warren of rabbits upset by a gun;
At BONG NUMBER TWO they were all in a stew,
Flinging cap after tunic and hose after shoe;
At BONG NUMBER THREE they were bare to the knee,
Undoing the doings as quick as could be;
At BONG NUMBER FOUR they were stripped to the core,
And pulling on nightshirts the wrong side before;
At BONG NUMBER FIVE they were looking alive,
And bizzing and buzzing like bees in a hive;
At BONG NUMBER SIX they gave themselves kicks,
Tripping over the rushes to snuff out the wicks;

At BONG NUMBER SEVEN, from Durham to Devon,
They slipped up a prayer to Our Father in Heaven;
And at BONG NUMBER EIGHT it was fatal to wait,
So with hearts beating all at a terrible rate,
In the deuce of a state, I need hardly relate,
They jumped Bong into bed like a bull at a gate.

ELEANOR AND HERBERT FARJEON

The Witches' Chant

Double, double, toil and trouble;
Fire, burn; and caldron, bubble!
   Fillet of a fenny snake,
   In the caldron boil and bake;
   Eye of newt, and toe of frog,
   Wool of bat, and tongue of dog,
   Adder's fork, and blind-worm's sting,
   Lizard's leg, and owlet's wing:
   For a **charm** of powerful trouble,
   Like a hell-broth boil and bubble.
Double, double toil and trouble,
Fire burn! and caldron, bubble!

WILLIAM SHAKESPEARE

An Old Woman of the Roads

O, to have a little house!
To own the hearth and stool and all!
The heaped-up sods upon the fire,
The pile of turf against the wall!

To have a clock with weights and chains
And pendulum swinging up and down!
A dresser filled with shining delph,
Speckled and white and blue and brown!

I could be busy all the day
Clearing and sweeping hearth and floor,
And fixing on their shelf again
My white and blue and speckled store!

I could be quiet there at night
Beside the fire and by myself
Sure of a bed and loth to leave
The ticking clock and shining delph!

Och! but I'm weary of mist and dark,
And roads where there's never a house nor bush,
And tired I am of bog and road,
And the crying wind and the lonesome hush!

And I am praying to God on high,
And I am praying Him night and day,
For a little house—a house of my own—
Out of the wind's and the rain's way.

PADRAIC COLUM

delph, crockery

Soldiers Come

Today, to be sure, the captain will come
At the head of his troop, with trumpet and drum;
Now, children, observe how he marches in state;
The man with the kettle-drum enters the gate;
Dub, dub, adub, dub. The trumpeters follow,
Tantara, tantara; while all the boys hollo!
See now comes the captain all daubed with gold lace;
Oh, what a grand gentleman; look in his face!
And see how he rides like a lord of the land,
With the fine flaming sword that he holds in his hand.
And his horse, the great creature, it prances and rears,
With ribbons in knots at its tail and its ears.

JONATHAN SWIFT

The Sea

I started early, took my dog,
And visited the sea;
The mermaids in the basement
Came out to look at me,

And frigates in the upper floor
Extended hempen hands,
Presuming me to be a mouse
Aground, upon the sands.

But no man moved me till the tide
Went past my simple shoe,
And past my apron and my belt,
And past my bodice too,

And made as he would eat me up
As wholly as a dew
Upon a dandelion's sleeve —
And then I started too.

And he — he followed close behind;
I felt his silver heel
Upon my ankle, — then my shoes
Would overflow with pearl.

Until we met the solid town,
No man he seemed to know;
And bowing with a mighty look
At me, the sea withdrew.

EMILY DICKINSON

Tartary

If I were Lord of Tartary,
  Myself and me alone,
My bed should be of ivory,
  Of beaten gold my throne;
And in my court should peacocks flaunt,
And in my forests tigers haunt,
And in my pools great fishes slant
  Their fins athwart the sun.

If I were Lord of Tartary,
  Trumpeters every day
To every meal should summon me,
  And in my courtyard bray;
And in the evening lamps would shine,
Yellow as honey, red as wine,
While harp, and flute, and mandoline,
  Made music sweet and gay.

If I were Lord of Tartary,
  I'd wear a robe of beads,
White, and gold, and green they'd be —
  And clustered thick as seeds;
And ere should wane the morning-star,
I'd don my robe and scimitar,
And zebras seven should draw my car
  Through Tartary's dark glades.

Lord of the fruit of Tartary,
  Her rivers silver-pale!
Lord of the hills of Tartary,
  Glen, thicket, wood, and dale!
Her flashing stars, her scented breeze,
Her trembling lakes, like foamless seas,
Her bird-delighting citron-trees
  In every purple vale!

WALTER DE LA MARE

93

Thady You Gander

Thaddaeus!
Don't stand there gawping,
Dance with me down through the maidens and men!
What are you waiting for?
You are the leader!
Dance them right round and back again!
Come to me quickly!
Arms furnish slickly!
Left with the girls
And come back to the middle!
Give me your right arm
And whirl me around!
Don't swing me so roughly,
I'm right off the ground!
Quick Thady!
You're all in a muddle,
Oh hurry, oh hurry,
The next couple's coming,
Get back in your rank now!
The boy will meander!
Oh Thady, you gander!

DAVID SHAVREEN

94

Tall Nettles

Tall nettles cover up, as they have done
These many springs, the rusty harrow, the plough
Long worn out, and the roller made of stone:
Only the elm butt tops the nettles now.

This corner of the farmyard I like most:
As well as any bloom upon a flower
I like the dust on the nettles, never lost
Except to prove the sweetness of a shower.

EDWARD THOMAS

Night Song

On moony nights the dogs bark shrill
Down the valley and up the hill.
    There's one who is angry to behold
The moon so unafraid and cold,
That makes the earth as bright as day,
But yet unhappy, dead, and grey.
    Another in his stray lair,
Says, 'Who's a-howling over there?
By heavens I will stop him soon
From interfering with the moon.'
    So back he barks, with throat upthrown;
'You leave our moon, our moon alone.'
And other distant dogs respond
Beyond the fields, beyond, beyond.

FRANCES CORNFORD

Great Lion

Shumba, the lion, has made his kill,
Has left his lair and drunk his fill.
And now he rests, and thinks of Man,
The thing that, since his life began,
He had avoided, even feared;
He, King of Beasts, who naught else feared!
He, Shumba, who has walked the wilds,
Had stalked his prey by blackest night,
He feared the puny weakling, Man!
Truly, Man's thunder-stick spoke high,
And bird and beast or buck might die
Who had but heard that fearful tongue
Which slew the old, which slew the young,
Which slew the kudu as they ran,
Which slew all things — yes, even Man!
But now the lion no longer feared;
He shakes his tawny mane and beard,
And lifts his head. To him, the cool
Forest seems strangely beautiful;

He wanders there, and silent stalks,
Head low, among the jungle walks.
These men are strange indeed. Though death
Comes from the thunder-sticks they bear,
They cannot hear the gasping breath
That shows a wounded buck is near.
They do not fight. They do not mate.
They cannot leap like streaks of light
Across the empty veld. And Fate
Has robbed them of their scent and sight.
So Shumba thinks. But now 'tis night.
The moon has risen. And the world
Is bathed in black and silver light.
And far away, an old baboon
Barks out a summons to his tribe.
And Shumba lifts his head and gives
His age-old salute to the moon.
Once more he lifts his maned head high—
Once more the throbbing echoes die;
And Shumba, satisfied, walks on.

ELIZABETH DU PREEZ

My Uncle Dan

My Uncle Dan's an inventor, you may think that's very fine.
You may wish he was your Uncle instead of being mine —
If he wanted he could make a watch that bounces when it drops,
He could make a helicopter out of string and bottle tops
Or any really useful thing you can't get in the shops.
  But Uncle Dan has other ideas:
  The bottomless glass for ginger beers,
  The toothless saw that's safe for the tree,
  A special word for a spelling bee
  (Like Lionocerangoutangadder),
  Or the roll-uppable rubber ladder,
  The mystery pie that bites when it's bit —
  My Uncle Dan invented it.
My Uncle Dan sits in his den inventing night and day.
His eyes peer from his hair and beard like mice from a load
  of hay.
And does he make the shoes that will go walks without your
  feet?
A shrinker to shrink instantly the elephants you meet?
A carver that just carves from the air steaks cooked and ready
  to eat?

  No, no, he has other intentions —
  Only perfectly useless inventions:
  Glassless windows (they never break),
  A medicine to cure the earthquake,
  The unspillable screwed-down cup,
  The stairs that go neither down nor up,
  The door you simply paint on a wall —
  Uncle Dan invented them all.

TED HUGHES

The Dismantled Ship

In some unused lagoon, some nameless bay,
On sluggish, lonesome water, anchor'd near the shore,
An old, dismasted, grey and batter'd ship, disabled, done,
After free voyages to all the seas of earth, haul'd up at last
    and hawser'd tight,
Lies rusting, mouldering.

WALT WHITMAN

The Winter is Past

... Lo, the winter is past,
The rain is over and gone;
The flowers appear on the earth;
The time of the singing of birds is come,
And the voice of the turtle is heard in our land;
The fig tree ripeneth her green figs,
And the vines are in blossom,
They give forth their fragrance.

THE BIBLE

Break of Day

The lark he rises early,
  And the ploughman goes away
Before it's morning fairly
  At the guessing break of day;
The fields lie in the dawning,
  And the valley's hid in gold,
At the pleasant time of morning
  When the shepherd goes to fold.
The maiden laughs and hollos
  When she sees the feeding cows;
They switch their tails and follow
  When she can't get over sloughs;
I love the gentle dawning,
  And the valleys hid in gold,
At the pleasant time of morning
  When the shepherd goes to fold.

JOHN CLARE

Summer Evening

Crows crowd croaking overhead,
Hastening to the woods to bed.
Cooing sits the lonely dove,
Calling home her absent love.
With 'Kirchup! Kirchup!' 'mong the wheats,
Partridge distant partridge greets.

Bats fly in hood and cowl;
Through the barn-hole pops the owl;
From the hedge, in drowsy hum,
Heedless buzzing beetles come,
Haunting every bushy place,
Flopping in the labourer's face.

Flowers now sleep within their hoods;
Daisies button into buds;
From soiling dew the buttercup
Shuts his golden jewels up;
And the rose and woodbine they
Wait again the smiles of day.

JOHN CLARE

A Snug Room

The view I behold on a sunshiny day
Is grand through the chimney-pots over the way.
This snug little chamber is crammed in all nooks
With worthless old knicknacks and silly old books,
Old armour, prints, pictures, pipes, china (all cracked),
Old rickety tables, and chairs broken-backed;
A bandy-legged, high-shouldered, worm-eaten seat
With a creaking old back, and twisted old feet.
And 'tis wonderful, surely, what music you get
From the rickety, ramshackle, wheezy spinet!

W. M. THACKERAY

Walking in the Dark

Her eyes the glow-worm lend thee,
The shooting-stars attend thee;
   And the elves also,
   Whose little eyes glow
Like the sparks of fire, befriend thee!

No will-o'-the-wisp mis-light thee;
Nor snake, or slow-worm bite thee;
   But on, on thy way
   Not making a stay,
Since ghost there's none to affright thee.

Let not the dark thee cumber;
What though the moon does slumber?
   The stars of the night
   Will lend thee their light,
Like tapers clear without number. . . .

ROBERT HERRICK

cumber, hinder

Drinking

The thirsty earth soaks up the rain,
And drinks, and gapes for drink again;
The plants suck in the earth, and are
With constant drinking fresh and fair;
The sea itself which one would think
Should have but little need of drink —
Drinks ten thousand rivers up,
So filled that they o'erflow the cup.

The busy sun—and one would guess
By's drunken fiery face no less—
Drinks up the sea, and when he's done,
The moon and stars drink up the sun:
They drink and dance by their own light,
They drink and revel all the night.

ABRAHAM COWLEY

Fairy Song

Over hill, over dale,
    Thorough bush, thorough briar,
Over park, over pale,
    Thorough flood, thorough fire:
I do wander everywhere,
Swifter than the moon's sphere;
And I serve the fairy queen,
To dew her orbs upon the green.
The cowslips tall her pensioners be;
In their gold coats spots you see;
Those be rubies, fairy favours,
In those freckles live their savours.

WILLIAM SHAKESPEARE

savours, scent

The Wind in a Frolic

The wind one morning sprang up from sleep,
Saying, 'Now for a frolic! now for a leap!'
So it swept with a bustle right through a great town,
Cracking the signs and scattering down
Shutters; and whisking, with merciless squalls,
Old women's bonnets and gingerbread stalls.
Then away to the fields it went blustering and humming,
And the cattle all wondered whatever was coming.
It was not too nice to hustle the bags
Of the beggar, and flutter his dirty rags.
Then it rushed like a monster on cottage and farm,
Striking their dwellings with sudden alarm.
The turkeys they gobbled, the geese screamed aloud,
And the hens crept to roost in a terrified crowd;
There was rearing of ladders, and logs laying on,
Where the thatch from the roof threatened soon to be gone.
But the wind had swept on, and had met in the lane
With a schoolboy, who panted and struggled in vain;
For it tossed him and twirled him, then passed, and he stood
With his hat in a pool, and his shoes in the mud.

WILLIAM HOWITT

The Sage's Pigtail

There was a sage in days of yore,
And he a handsome pigtail wore;
But wondered much and sorrowed more
   Because it hung behind him.

He mused upon this curious case,
And swore he'd change the pigtail's place,
And have it hanging at his face,
   Not dangling there behind him.

Says he, 'The mystery I've found;
I'll turn me round'—he turned him round;
   But still it hung behind him.

Then round and round, and out and in,
All day the puzzled sage did spin;
In vain—it mattered not a pin—
   The pigtail hung behind him.

And right and left, and round about,
And up and down, and in and out,
He turned; but still the pigtail stout
   Hung steadily behind him.

And though his efforts never slack,
And though he twist and twirl and tack,
Alas! Still faithful to his back,
   The pigtail hangs behind him.

W. M. THACKERAY

Robin Hood's Golden Prize

I have heard talk of bold Robin Hood,
    And of brave Little John,
Of Friar Tuck, and Will Scarlet,
    Locksley, and Maid Marion.

But such a tale as this before
    I think there was never none;
For Robin Hood disguised himself,
    And to the wood is gone.

Like to a friar, bold Robin Hood
    Was accoutréd in his array;
With hood, gown, beads and crucifix,
    He passed upon the way.

He had not gone miles two or three,
    But it was his chance to spy
Two lusty priests, clad all in black,
    Come riding gallantly.

'Benedicie,' then said Robin Hood,
    'Some pity on me take;
Cross you my hand with a silver groat,
    For Our dear Lady's sake!

'For I have been wandering all this day,
    And nothing could I get;
Not so much as one poor cup of drink,
    Nor bit of bread to eat.'

'By my Holy Dame,' the priests replied,
  'We never a penny have;
For we this morning have been robbed,
  And could no money save.'

'I am much afraid,' said bold Robin Hood,
  'That you both do tell a lie;
And now before that you go hence,
  I am resolved to try.'

When as these priests heard him say so,
  They rode away amain;
But Robin betook him to his heels,
  And soon overtook them again.

Then Robin Hood laid hold of them both,
  And pulled them down from their horse:
'O spare us, friar!' the priests cried out,
  'On us have some remorse!'

'You said you had no money,' quoth he;
  'Wherefore, without delay,
We three will fall down on our knees,
  And for money we will pray.'

The priests they could not him gainsay,
  But down they kneeled with speed;
'Send us, O send us,' then quoth they,
  'Some money to serve our need!'

The priests did pray with mournful face,
  Sometimes their hands did wring,
Sometimes they wept and cried aloud,
  Whilst Robin did merrily sing.

When they had prayed an hour's space,
  The priests did still lament;
Then quoth bold Robin, 'Now let's see
  What money heaven hath sent.

'We will be sharers, all alike,
    Of the money that we have;
And there is never a one of us
    That his fellows shall deceive.'

The priests their hands in their pockets put,
    But money would find none:
'We'll search ourselves,' said Robin Hood,
    'Each other, one by one.'

Then Robin took pains to search them both,
    And he found good store of gold;
Five hundred pieces presently
    Upon the grass were told.

'Here's a brave show,' said Robin Hood,
    'Such store of gold to see!
And you shall each one have a part,
    As you prayed so heartily.'

He gave them fifty pound a-piece,
    And the rest for himself did keep;
The priests they durst not speak one word,
    But they sighed wondrous deep.

He set them upon their horses again,
    And away then they did ride;
And he returned to the merry green-wood,
    With great joy, mirth and pride.

The Kite

It is a hard climb to the top of this high hill.
Grasping our kite we mount in face of a wind
Which parches the cheek, steals away smell and hearing,
And drowns the lark's call.

At last the summit! Here we may breathe, arching
Our backs to the blast. And see! fields, far-below poplars!
Cloud-shadows racing, tree-shadows held! One minute
All's shadow, then sunlight all!

Set the kite free! The snow-white frame released
Leaps to the snatch of the wind. With strong intent,
High to the blue-lit sky it soars, and there
Strains in the steady squall.

All a long day to curb and control its flight!
And nothing shall mar this long-looked-for delight.
Let never our arms and legs be weary; nor let
This fair wind slacken and fall!

JOHN WALSH

The Serpent

Wake the serpent not—lest he
Should not know the way to go—
Let him crawl which yet lies sleeping
Through the deep grass of the meadow!
Not a bee shall hear him creeping,
Not a may-fly shall awaken
From its cradling blue-bell shaken,
Not the starlight as he's sliding
Through the grass with silent gliding.

PERCY BYSSHE SHELLEY

Anything may happen when . . .

. . . When nettles in winter bring forth roses red,
   And all manner of thorn-trees bear figs naturally,
And geese bear pearls in every mead,
   And laurels bear cherries abundantly,
   And oaks bear dates very plenteously.

When thistles bear berries in every place,
   And herrings their horns in forests boldly blow,
And bulls of the sea sing a good bass,
   And whiting shoot rooks out of a crossbow,
   And goslings hunt the wolf to overthrow.

When crows catch salmon in woods and parks,
   And are caught by swifts and snails,
And camels in the air catch swallows and larks,
   And mice move mountains by wagging of their tails,
   And shipmen take sour crabs instead of sails.

To my Sister

It is the first mild day of March:
Each minute sweeter than before,
The redbreast sings from the tall larch
That stands beside our door.

There is a blessing in the air,
Which seems a sense of joy to yield
To the bare trees, and mountains bare,
And grass in the green field. . . .

WILLIAM WORDSWORTH

Jack and Joan

Jack and Joan they think no ill,
But loving live, and merry still;
Do their week-days' work, and pray
Devoutly on the holy day:
Skip and trip it on the green,
And help to choose the Summer Queen;
Lash out, at a country feast,
Their silver penny with the best.

THOMAS CAMPION

The Lumbermen's Camp

(Song of the Broad-axe)

Lumbermen in their winter camp, day-break in the woods, stripes
   of snow on the limbs of trees, the occasional snapping,
The glad clear sound of one's voice, the merry song, the natural
   life of the woods, the strong day's work,
The blazing fire at night, the sweet taste of supper, the talk, the
   bed of hemlock boughs, and the bear-skin.

WALT WHITMAN

III

Releasing a Migrant 'Yen' (Wild Goose)

At Nine Rivers, in the tenth year, in winter,—heavy snow;
The river-water covered with ice and the forests broken with
    their load.
The birds of the air, hungry and cold, went flying east and west;
And with them flew a migrant 'yen', loudly clamouring for food.
Among the snow it pecked for grass; and rested on the surface of
    the ice:
It tried with its wings to scale the sky; but its tired flight was
    slow.
The boys of the river spread a net and caught the bird as it flew;
They took it in their hands to the city-market and sold it there
    alive.
I that was once a man of the North am now an exile here:
Bird and man, in their different kind, are each strangers in the
    south.
And because the sight of an exiled bird wounded an exile's heart,
I paid your ransom and set you free, and you flew away to the
    clouds.

Chinese Poem,
translated by ARTHUR WALEY

Lovely Notes

Thus I went wide—where, walking alone,
In a wide wilderness, by a wood side,
Bliss of the birds' song made me abide there,
And on a lawn under a linden I leaned awhile
To listen to their lays, their lovely notes;
The mirth of their mouths made me to sleep,
And mid that bliss I dreamed—marvellously.

WILLIAM LANGLAND

The Wild Boar

On his bow-back he hath a battle set
  Of bristly pikes, that ever threat his foes;
His eyes, like glow-worms, shine when he doth fret;
  His snout digs sepulchres where'er he goes;
    Being moved, he strikes whate'er is in his way,
    And whom he strikes his crooked tushes slay.

His brawny sides, with hairy bristles armed,
  Are better proof than thy spear's point can enter;
His short thick neck cannot be easily harmed;
  Being ireful, on the lion he will venter:
    The thorny brambles and embracing bushes,
    As fearful of him, part; through which he rushes.

WILLIAM SHAKESPEARE

battle, battlement, like the top of a castle
ireful, angry   *venter*, venture, dare to rush

The Children Rebel

Easily the thing was done,
For the children were more than two to one;

Brave as lions, quick as foxes,
With hoards of wealth in their money-boxes!

They seized the keys, they patrolled the street,
They drove the policeman off his beat,

They built barricades, they stationed sentries —
You must give the word when you came to the entries.

They dressed themselves in the Riflemen's clothes,
They had pea-shooters, they had arrows and bows.

They went to the schoolroom and tore the books,
They munched the puffs at the pastrycook's.

They sucked the jam, they lost the spoons,
They sent up several fire-balloons,

They let off crackers, they burnt a guy,
They piled a bonfire fifty feet high;

Nailed up the doors, slid down the stairs,
Sawed off the legs of the parlour chairs;

They offered a prize for the laziest boy,
And one for the most magnificent toy.

They passed a law to have always plenty
Of beautiful things: we shall mention twenty:

A magic lantern for all to see,
Rabbits to keep, and a Christmas tree,

A boat, a house that went on wheels,
An organ to grind, and sherry at meals,

Drums and wheelbarrows, Roman candles,
Whips with whistles let into the handles;

A real live giant, a roc to fly,
A goat to tease, a bottomless pie,

A garret of apples, a box of paints,
A saw and a hammer, and *no complaints*.

They never waited for king or for cat;
They never wiped their shoes on the mat;

Their joy was great; their joy was greater:
They rode in the baby's perambulator!

Forty-five fiddlers to play the fiddle;
Right foot, left foot, down the middle;

Conjuring tricks with poker and tongs;
Riddles and forfeits, singing of songs.

The Queen is Jill and the King is John:
I trust the Government will go on!

W. B. RANDS

Youth and Age

Impatient of his childhood,
  'Ah me!' exclaims young Arthur
Whilst roving in the wild wood,
  'I wish I were my father!'
Meanwhile, to see his Arthur
  So skip, and play, and run,
'Ah me!' exclaims the father,
  'I wish I were my son!'

THOMAS HOOD

Meet-on-the-Road

'Now, pray, where are you going?'
  said Meet-on-the-Road.

'To school, sir, to school, sir,'
  said Child-as-it-Stood.

'What have you in your basket, child?'
  said Meet-on-the-Road.

'My dinner, sir, my dinner, sir,'
  said Child-as-it-Stood.

'What have you for dinner, child?'
  said Meet-on-the-Road.

'Some pudding, sir, some pudding, sir,'
  said Child-as-it-Stood.

'Oh, then I pray, give me a share,'
  said Meet-on-the-Road.

'I've little enough for myself, sir,'
  said Child-as-it-Stood.

'What have you got that cloak on for?'
  said Meet-on-the-Road.

'To keep the wind and cold from me,'
  said Child-as-it-Stood.

'I wish the wind would blow through you,'
  said Meet-on-the-Road

'Oh, what a wish! What a wish!'
  said Child-as-it-Stood.

'Pray what are those bells ringing for?'
  said Meet-on-the-Road.

'To ring bad spirits home again,'
  said Child-as-it-Stood.

'Oh, then I must be going, child!'
  said Meet-on-the-Road.

'So fare you well, so fare you well,'
  said Child-as-it-Stood.

Index of First Lines

ACKNOWLEDGEMENTS

The editors make grateful acknowledgement to the following for permission to reprint copyright material:

The Cresset Press for 'Night Song' and 'A Child's Dream' by Frances Cornford; Mrs H. M. Davies and Jonathan Cape Ltd for 'Winter's Beauty' from the *Collected Poems* of W. H. Davies; The Literary Trustees of Walter de la Mare and the Society of Authors as their representative for 'The Prince', 'Trees' and 'Tartary'; Harvard University Press for two poems from *The Poems of Emily Dickinson*; J. J. du Preez for Elizabeth du Preez's 'Great Lion'; David Higham Associates Ltd for 'William I' from *Kings and Queens*, 'Kingcups in Town' from *The Children's Bells* and 'House Hunters' from *Then There Were Three* by Eleanor Farjeon; Macmillan & Co Ltd for 'Sight' from *Collected Poems 1905–1925* of Wilfrid Gibson; International Authors N.V. for 'Allie' from *The Penny Fiddle* by Robert Graves; Macmillan & Co Ltd and the Trustees of the Hardy Estate for 'The Fallow Deer at the Lonely House' from *The Collected Poems of Thomas Hardy*; Ted Hughes and Faber & Faber Ltd for 'Folks' and 'My Uncle Dan' from *Meet My Folks*; Basil Blackwell for 'Earth's Motion' and 'Two Winter Joys' by Mrs E. L. M. King; Ogden Nash and J. M. Dent & Sons Ltd for 'The Bat' from *The Private Dining Room* and 'The Egg' from *The Face is Familiar*; James Reeves and Oxford University Press for 'Cows' from *The Blackbird in the Lilac* and 'The Old Wife and the Ghost' from *Hurdy-Gurdy*; Ian Serraillier and Oxford University Press for 'The Hen and the Carp' from *Thomas and the Sparrow*; Theodore Roethke and A. M. Heath & Company Ltd for 'The Cow'; A. L. Rowse and Faber & Faber Ltd for 'How Many Miles to Mylor' from *Poems of a Decade*; David Shavreen for 'Thady You Gander'; Mrs Iris Wise and Macmillan & Co Ltd for 'The Fur Coat', 'Seamus Beg' and 'The Snare' from the *Collected Poems* of James Stephens; Faber & Faber Ltd for 'Ploughing on Sunday' from *Selected Poems* of Wallace Stevens; Mrs Helen Thomas and Faber & Faber Ltd for 'If I Should Ever' and 'Tall Nettles' by Edward Thomas; Arthur Waley and Constable & Company Ltd for lines from 'Releasing A Migrant "Yen"' from 170 *Chinese Poems*; John Walsh and Oxford University Press for 'The Kite' from *The Roundabout by the Sea*; John Walsh and William Heinemann Ltd for 'Peter to Tea' from *The Truants*; Mrs W. B. Yeats and Macmillan & Co Ltd for 'The Song of the Old Mother' from *The Collected Poems of W. B. Yeats*; Alexander Gray for 'On a Cat Ageing'.